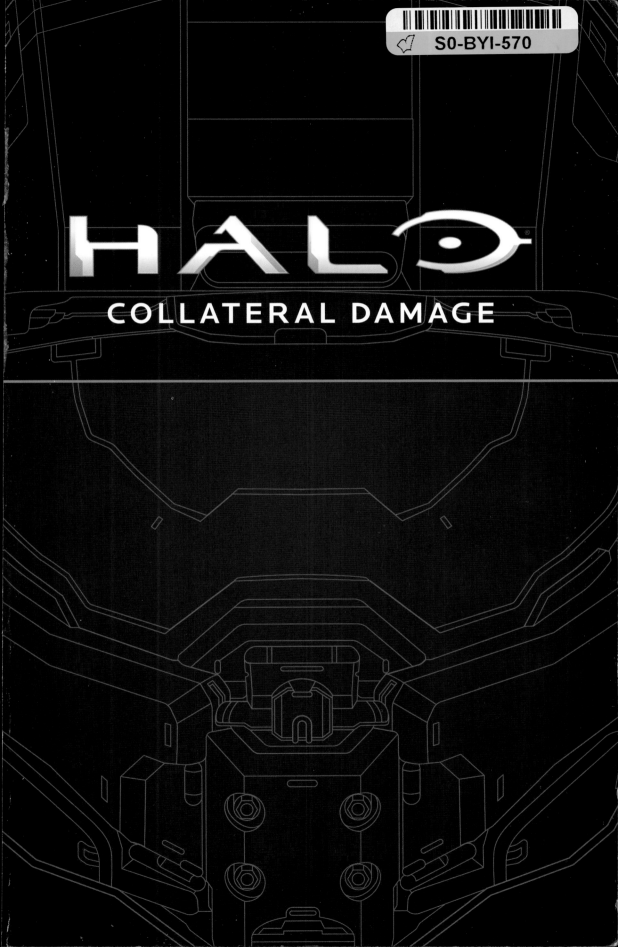

HALO®

COLLATERAL DAMAGE

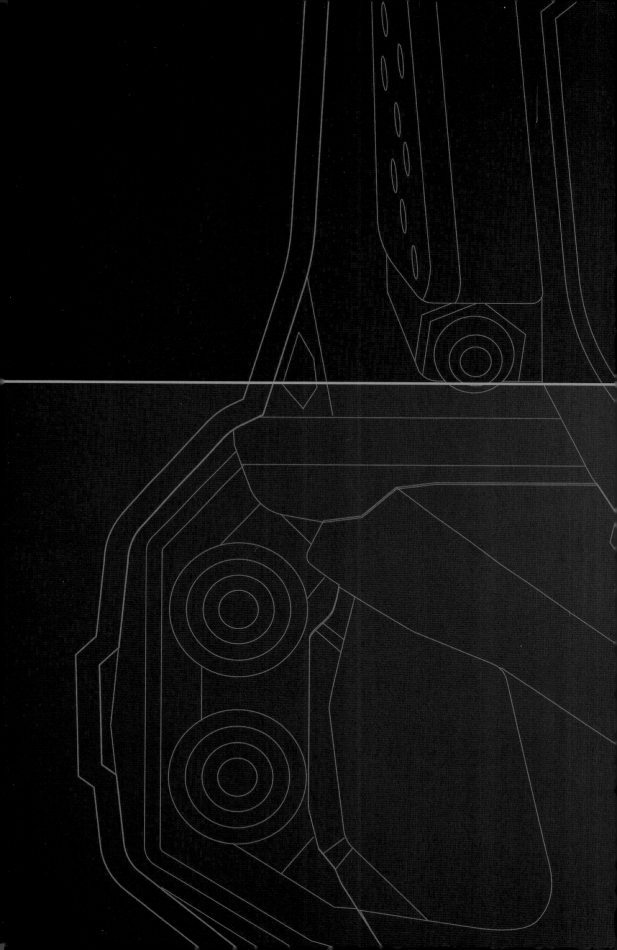

HALO
COLLATERAL DAMAGE

SCRIPT
ALEX IRVINE

PENCILS
DAVE CROSLAND

INKS
DAVE CROSLAND
(CHAPTERS 1, 2 & 3)
SHERARD JACKSON
(CHAPTER 3)

COLORS
LEONARD O'GRADY
(CHAPTERS 1, 2 & 3)
DAN JACKSON
(CHAPTER 3)

LETTERING
SIMON BOWLAND

FRONT COVER ART
ZAK HARTONG

DARK HORSE BOOKS

PRESIDENT AND PUBLISHER
MIKE RICHARDSON

EDITOR
SPENCER CUSHING

ASSISTANT EDITOR
KEVIN BURKHALTER

COLLECTION DESIGNER
PATRICK SATTERFIELD

DIGITAL ART TECHNICIAN
JOSIE CHRISTENSEN

HALO: COLLATERAL DAMAGE
HALO © 2018 MICROSOFT CORPORATION. ALL RIGHTS RESERVED. MICROSOFT, HALO, THE HALO LOGO, AND 343 INDUSTRIES ARE TRADEMARKS OF THE MICROSOFT GROUP OF COMPANIES. DARK HORSE COMICS® IS A TRADEMARK OF DARK HORSE COMICS, INC., REGISTERED IN VARIOUS CATEGORIES AND COUNTRIES. ALL RIGHTS RESERVED. NO PORTION OF THIS PUBLICATION MAY BE REPRODUCED OR TRANSMITTED, IN ANY FORM OR BY ANY MEANS, WITHOUT THE EXPRESS WRITTEN PERMISSION OF DARK HORSE COMICS, INC. NAMES, CHARACTERS, PLACES, AND INCIDENTS FEATURED IN THIS PUBLICATION EITHER ARE THE PRODUCT OF THE AUTHOR'S IMAGINATION OR ARE USED FICTITIOUSLY. ANY RESEMBLANCE TO ACTUAL PERSONS (LIVING OR DEAD), EVENTS, INSTITUTIONS, OR LOCALES, WITHOUT SATIRIC INTENT, IS COINCIDENTAL.

THIS VOLUME COLLECTS ISSUES #1 THROUGH #3 OF THE DARK HORSE COMIC-BOOK SERIES *HALO: COLLATERAL DAMAGE*.

SPECIAL THANKS TO TYLER JEFFERS, SCOTT JOBE, CARLOS NARANJO, TIFFANY O'BRIEN, FRANK O'CONNOR, JEREMY PATENAUDE, KENNETH PETERS, CORRINNE ROBINSON, SPARTH, AND KIKI WOLFKILL AT MICROSOFT.

PUBLISHED BY DARK HORSE BOOKS
A DIVISION OF DARK HORSE COMICS, INC.
10956 SE MAIN STREET
MILWAUKIE, OR 97222

DARKHORSE.COM
HALOWAYPOINT.COM

TO FIND A COMICS SHOP IN YOUR AREA, VISIT COMICSHOPLOCATOR.COM

SCHOLASTIC EDITION: SEPTEMBER 2018
ISBN 978-1-50671-115-7

10 9 8 7 6 5 4 3 2 1
PRINTED IN CANADA

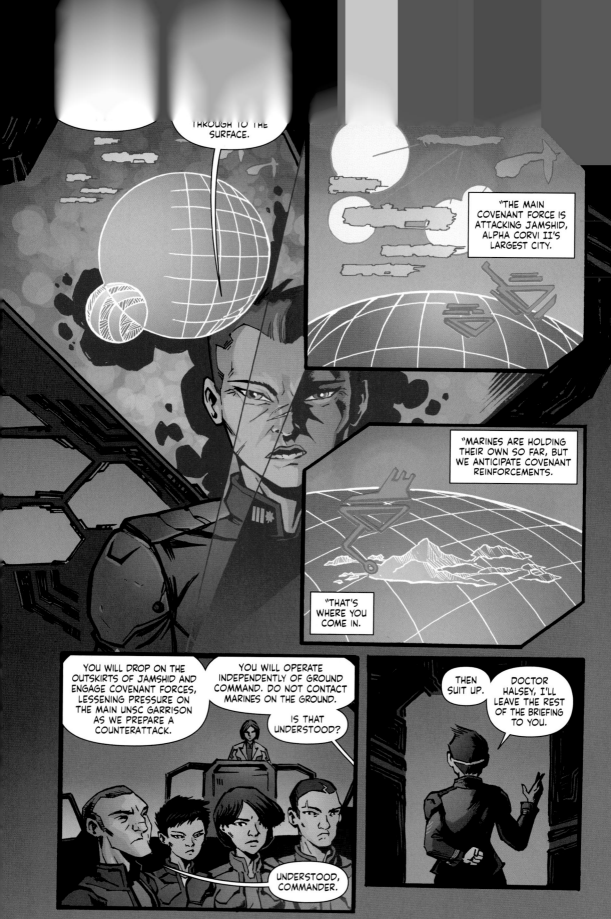

THROUGH TO THE SURFACE.

"THE MAIN COVENANT FORCE IS ATTACKING JAMSHID, ALPHA CORVI II'S LARGEST CITY.

"MARINES ARE HOLDING THEIR OWN SO FAR, BUT WE ANTICIPATE COVENANT REINFORCEMENTS.

"THAT'S WHERE YOU COME IN.

YOU WILL DROP ON THE OUTSKIRTS OF JAMSHID AND ENGAGE COVENANT FORCES, LESSENING PRESSURE ON THE MAIN UNSC GARRISON AS WE PREPARE A COUNTERATTACK.

YOU WILL OPERATE INDEPENDENTLY OF GROUND COMMAND. DO NOT CONTACT MARINES ON THE GROUND.

IS THAT UNDERSTOOD?

UNDERSTOOD, COMMANDER.

THEN SUIT UP.

DOCTOR HALSEY, I'LL LEAVE THE REST OF THE BRIEFING TO YOU.

WE HAVE TO DEFEND BLACK REEF, BUT WE ALSO WANT TO KNOW WHY THE COVENANT IS TARGETING IT.

WE KNOW VERY LITTLE ABOUT THE COVENANT. PAY CLOSE ATTENTION TO THEIR TACTICS, THEIR UNIT COMPOSITION, THEIR WEAPONS AND TECHNOLOGY.

"ALSO NEUTRALIZE THEM, RIGHT?"

"YES, SPARTAN-104. THAT IS STILL YOUR PRIMARY OBJECTIVE."

BUT WHILE YOU ARE NEUTRALIZING THEM, SEE IF YOU CAN LEARN WHY THEY TARGETED THIS MINE. THEY'RE NOT THERE BY ACCIDENT.

OH, AND ONE MORE THING. DON'T EXPECT ANY HELP FROM MARINES ON THE GROUND. THEY'VE GOT ALL THEY CAN HANDLE WITH THE COVENANT.

"COMMAND DOESN'T WANT THEIR DEPLOYED TROOPS INTERACTING WITH SPARTANS."

"UNDERSTOOD. WE'RE ON OUR OWN."

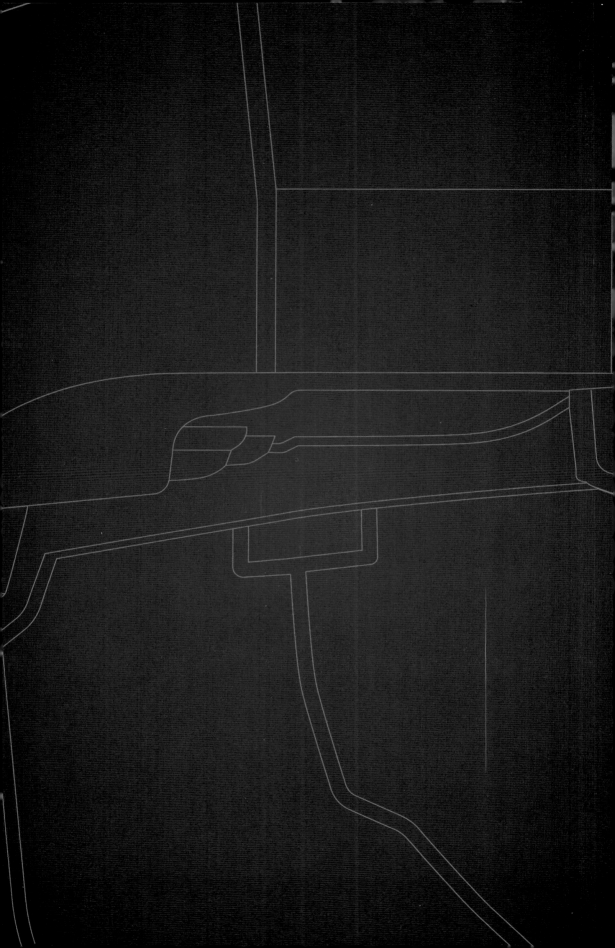

"I'D HATE TO GET SANDWICHED DOWN HERE."

WE'RE NOT GOING TO BE ABLE TO HOLD THE ENTRANCE.

WE NEED TO GET OUT OF HERE, CAP.

TO WHERE? THIS IS THE FIGHT. WE DON'T WIN IT HERE, WE'RE ALL GOING TO DIE.

ALL DUE RESPECT, CAP, THE ALIENS DON'T CARE ABOUT US. THEY WANT DOWN IN THE MINE.

WE BLOW THE ENTRANCE, THEY'RE TRAPPED. THEY HAVE TO TURN AND FIGHT.

AND THE MARINES DOWN IN THE MINE ARE SOL.

FRAN, GET THE JACKHAMMER.

IT'S OUR LAST ONE.

I KNOW. MIGUEL, TAKE TWO SATCHEL CHARGES.

WE BLOW IT NOW, WE TRAP THAT FORCE DOWN IN THE MINE. THEN WE HANDLE WHAT'S LEFT.

YOU GONNA LEAVE ONLY FOUR OF THEM AGAINST ALL THOSE COVENANT?

"NO. WE ARE GOING TO KEEP THE ENEMY FROM THEIR OBJECTIVE."

NOW, FRAN!

DANGER
FLAMMABLE

FOOM

FOOM

COME ON!

00:01

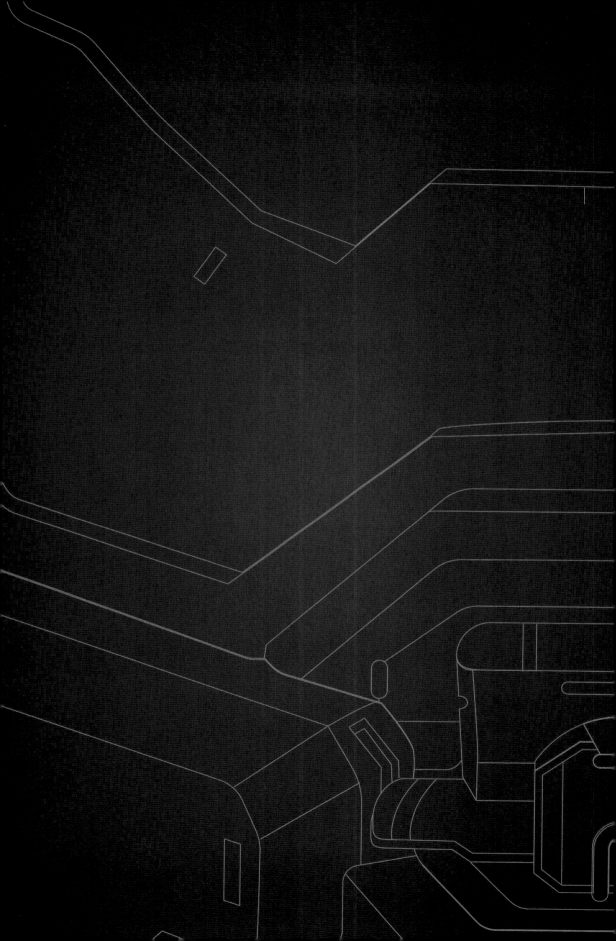

"WE NEED TO HURRY."

THESE SHOULD DO THE TRICK.

ONE SECOND.

HALSEY WILL WANT TO SEE THIS.

GOOD IDEA. HUG THE WALL.

THAT OUGHT TO BE THE LAST OF THEM.

GOOD TO SEE ALL FOUR OF YOU COMING BACK.

YOU LEFT THEM THERE. THEY FOUGHT FOR US AND YOU LEFT THEM THERE.

THEY DON'T MATTER. NOT IN THE BIG PICTURE.

WE LOST THIS BATTLE. BUT IT'S ONE SMALL PART OF A MUCH LARGER WAR.

THAT WAR IS BIGGER THAN THIS PLANET. IT'S BIGGER THAN ANY ONE LIFE. EVEN BIGGER THAN ANY ONE SPARTAN.

WE'RE FIGHTING FOR THE SURVIVAL OF HUMAN CIVILIZATION.

ALL DUE RESPECT, MA'AM, THEY FOUGHT FOR US AND WE SHOULD HAVE FOUGHT FOR THEM.

THAT WILL BE ENOUGH, SOLDIER.

JOHN. YOU BROUGHT YOUR TEAM BACK SAFE. THAT'S WHAT MATTERS.

THERE WILL ALWAYS BE SOME COLLATERAL DAMAGE.

"NOW TELL ME: WHAT WERE THEY LOOKING FOR DOWN IN THE MINE?"

END.

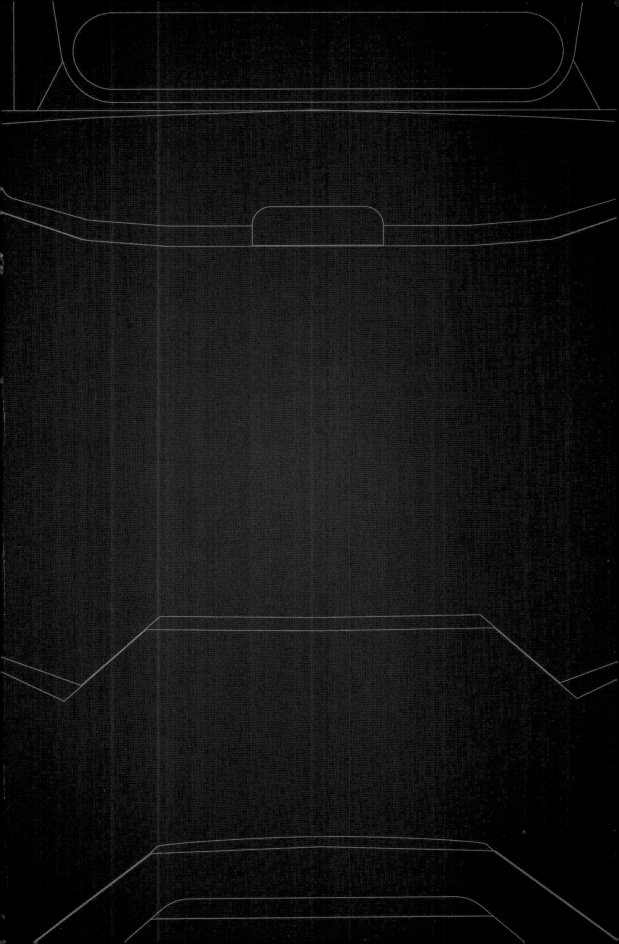

HALO

HALO: RISE OF ATRIOX
CULLEN BUNN // JOHN JACKSON MILLER
JONATHAN WAYSHAK // AND OTHERS

The story of Atriox, his rise to power, his contempt for the Covenant, and the formation of the Banished is told across this five-chapter anthology featuring characters and stories from *Halo Wars 2*.

$19.99 | ISBN 978-1-50670-494-4

HALO: FALL OF REACH
BRIAN REED // FELIX RUIZ
ISAAC HANNAFORD // VAL STAPLES

In the year 2517, humanity's last hope is with Dr. Catherine Halsey, the SPARTAN-II program, and a six-year-old boy: John-117. Kidnapped and ruthlessly trained, John endures and rises as the leader of the Spartans: he becomes the Master Chief! These legendary heroes are entrusted with stopping the Covenant at all costs!

$24.99 | ISBN 978-1-50670-077-9

HALO: COLLATERAL DAMAGE
ALEX IRVINE // DAVE CROSLAND
SHERARD JACKSON

Petty Officer John-117 and Blue Team are deployed to Alpha Corvi II to halt the Covenant's efforts to uncover something hidden below the planet's surface. The team realizes they have to rely on each other (and a small cadre of human rebels) to survive and complete their mission!

$14.99 | ISBN 978-1-50670-747-1

HALO: LIBRARY EDITION
DUFFY BOUDREAU // DOUGLAS FRANCHIN
BRIAN REED // SERGIO ARIÑO // AND OTHERS

The entirety of the *Initiation* and *Escalation* series in deluxe, definitive editions! Features exclusive annotations, complete cover galleries, and behind-the-scenes extras!

VOLUME 1 | $49.99 | ISBN 978-1-61655-907-6
VOLUME 2 | $49.99 | ISBN 978-1-50670-234-6

HALO: UNSC *VULTURE* SHIP REPLICA
The *Vulture* is heavily featured in the hit game *Halo Wars 2*, and now you can own this beautifully detailed polyresin, limited edition 6" replica.

$49.99 | ISBN 978-1-61659-797-9

HALO: UNSC *SPIRIT OF FIRE* SHIP REPLICA
The *Spirit of Fire* is a heavily upgraded Phoenix-class colonial support vessel, and this highly detailed 8" replica captures its fighting spirit.

$49.99 | ISBN 978-1-61659-651-4

DARKHORSE.COM | HALOWAYPOINT.COM